What am I? Riddles and Brainteasers for Kids St. Patrick's Day Edition

C Langkamp

Published in Columbus Ohio

February 2017

ziggyzigfreed@gmail.com

Introduction

This book consists of simple questions and answers all dealing with St. Patrick's Day. It is intended for fun, learning and enjoyment. It can be used as a teaching guide to help children who are just learning how to formulate sentences, words, and phrases as well as understanding more about this special holiday. The answers to each question help students write sentences based on the original questions, a technique that is called "Turn The Question Around".

Enjoy!

What Am I? St. Patrick's Day Riddle #1

What am I?

This is what someone might do to you if you do not wear green on St Patrick's Day!

What am I?

What Am I? St. Patrick's Day Riddle #2

What am I?

It is good luck if you find me with 4 leaves. I am green and grow outside. The author has never seen one with 4 leaves, only 3.

What am I?

What Am I? St. Patrick's Day Riddle #3

What am I?

I am full of mischief. I look like a little elf. Also, it is believed that I make shoes.

What am I?

What Am I? St. Patrick's Day Riddle #4

What am I?

I am said to be found at the end of a rainbow. Anyone who finds me will be very happy!

What am I?

What Am I? St. Patrick's Day Riddle #5

What am I?

On a day that is both rainy and sunny, you might see me. I am filled with color.

What am I?

What Am I? St. Patrick's Day Riddle #6

What am I?

People dress up and build floats to walk, dance and participate in this activity.

What am I?

What Am I? St. Patrick's Day Riddle #7

What am I?

This is a common meal found on St. Patrick's Day. It is believed to be an Irish dish.

What am I?

What Am I? St. Patrick's Day Riddle #8

What am I?

I am the country in the United Kingdom that is where St Patrick's Day first began.

What am I?

What Am I? St. Patrick's Day Riddle #9

What am I?

Lots of adults like to drink this green alcoholic beverage to celebrate!

What am I?

What Am I? St. Patrick's Day Riddle #10

What am I?

I am the patron Saint who taught the Irish people about Christianity. I am the person the holiday is named after.

What am I?

Answer to St. Patrick's Day Riddle #1

What am I?

This is what someone might do to you if you do not wear green on St Patrick's Day!

What am I?

I am a pinching person! I will pinch you for not wearing green!

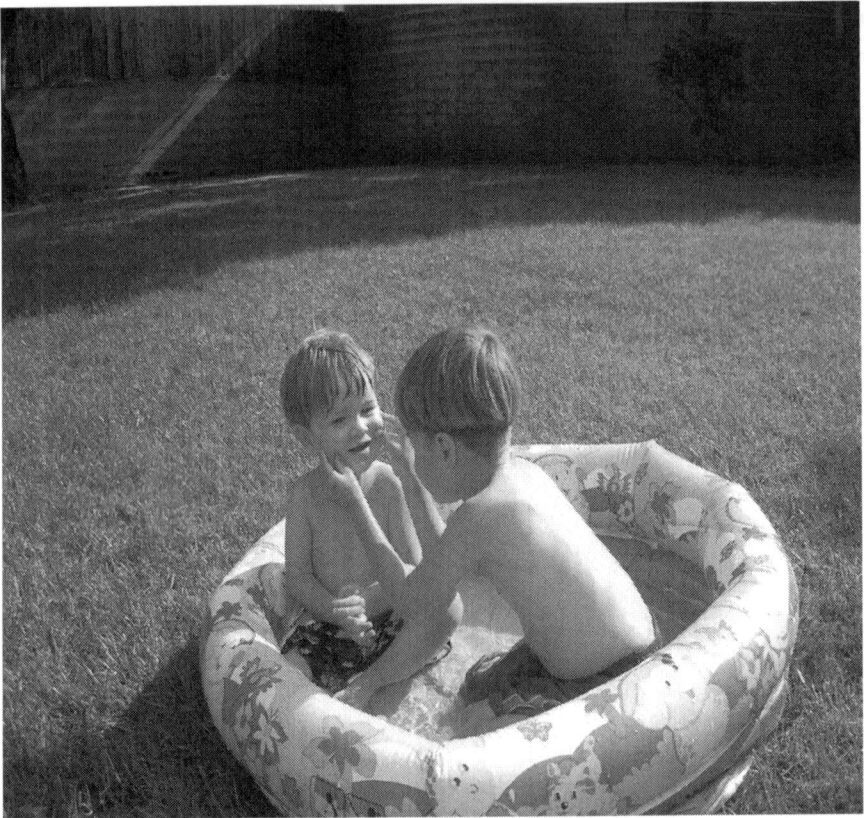

Answer to St. Patrick's Day Riddle #2

What am I?

It is good luck if you find me with 4 leaves. I am green and grow outside. The author has never seen one with 4 leaves, only 3.

What am I?

I am a 4 leaf clover. Three leaf clovers are very common!

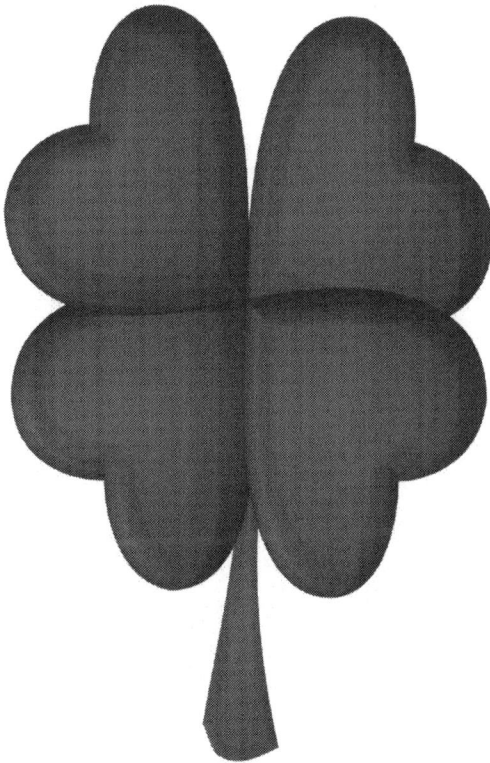

Answer to St. Patrick's Day Riddle #3

What am I?

I am full of mischief. I look like a little elf. Also, it is believed that I make shoes.

What am I?

I am a leprechaun.

Answer to St. Patrick's Day Riddle #4

What am I?

I am said to be found at the end of a rainbow. Anyone who finds me will be very happy!

What am I?

I am a pot of gold!

Answer to St. Patrick's Day Riddle #5

What am I?

On a day that is both rainy and sunny, you might see me. I am filled with color.

What am I?

I am a rainbow.

Answer to St. Patrick's Day Riddle #6

What am I?

People dress up and build floats to walk, dance and participate in this activity.

What am I?

I am a parade.

Answer to St. Patrick's Day Riddle #7

What am I?

This is a common meal found on St. Patrick's Day. It is believed to be an Irish dish.

What am I?

I am corned beef and cabbage.

Answer to St. Patrick's Day Riddle #8

What am I?

I am the country in the United Kingdom that is where St Patrick's Day first began.

What am I?

I am Ireland.

Answer to St. Patrick's Day Riddle #9

What am I?

Lots of adults like to drink this green alcoholic beverage to celebrate!

What am I?

I am green beer.

Answer to St. Patrick's Day Riddle #10

What am I?

I am the patron Saint who taught the Irish people about Christianity. I am the person the holiday is named after.

What am I?

I am Saint Patrick!

Thank You

I hope you have enjoyed reading this book as much as I have enjoyed writing it. Please let me know your thoughts, suggestions, and comments by contacting me at ziggyzigfreed@gmail.com. All email will be answered.

Please check out my other What Am I? books at https://www.amazon.com/-/e/B01M3V2KS3.

Have a wonder filled day!

Made in the USA
Middletown, DE
16 February 2018